D0505865

away

Tessa Krailing

WELLINGTON SQUARE

Contents

The football match

'Who's playing? Who's playing?' said Kevin.
The kids were looking at the notice that
Mr March had put up.
It said,

FOOTBALL MATCH
_____

WATERLOO SCHOOL
v.
RIPTON ROVERS
AT RIPTON SCHOOL
SAT 10th APRIL
KICK-OFF 2 O'CLOCK
PLAYERS
RYAN ANDREWS
BRIAN DENNIS

Then there was a list of names.
It was a list of the boys who were playing
in the match.
'I'm playing!' shouted Rocky.
'So are Ben and Tony.
And you are, Kevin.'
'Great!' said Kevin. 'We're sure to win!'

Mr Belter and Mr March went with the football
team to Ripton School.
It was about four miles away, in
a different part of town.
Some of the other kids had come along to
cheer on the team.
'We're going to win,' said Kevin. 'It'll be easy.'
'Now, Kevin,' said Mr March.
'I want a good, clean match.
No rough stuff, OK? A good, clean match and
lots of goals.'

The referee got the teams together.
'Now,' he said, 'no rough play and no fouls.
If anyone fouls I'll put his name in my little
red book. OK?
Right! Let's get ready to play!'

7

The referee blew his whistle and
the match started.

Kevin got the ball.
He kicked it to Tony and Tony kicked
it to Rocky.
Kevin ran towards the goal and Rocky kicked
the ball to him.
A player from the other team ran up to Kevin.
'Out of my way!' shouted Kevin.
'I've got the ball. I'm going to get a goal.'
Kevin pushed the other boy and he fell over.

The referee blew his whistle.
'Foul!' he shouted.
He put Kevin's name in his little red book.
'If you do that again,' he said to Kevin,
'you'll be sent off.'

The match started again.
Ripton Rovers had the ball, then Waterloo School
got it.
Tony ran towards the goal with the ball.
He kicked it to Rocky.

Rocky was right in front of the goal.
He kicked the ball hard.
The goalkeeper couldn't save it.

'We've got a goal!' shouted Jamila.
'Rocky got a goal!'
'We're winning,' said Tessa.
'Waterloo School one, Ripton Rovers nil.'
Everyone from Waterloo School cheered.

Kevin is sent off

Kevin wasn't pleased that Rocky had got a goal.
He wanted to get all the goals himself.
He had to get the ball back.
Kevin tried very hard but he couldn't
get the ball.
The next time he tried to get the ball
he knocked a boy over.
Another foul!

The referee blew his whistle.
'I told you,' he said.
'I told you not to foul again.
I'm going to send you off.
Leave the pitch at once, please.'

'Stupid boy,' said Mr Belter as Kevin
walked by him.
'Mr March told you we wanted a clean game.'
'Now we only have ten players,' said Tessa.
'How can we win with only ten players?'

Kevin was fed up.
Everyone was angry with him and the team
had only ten players.
Waterloo School would never win now!

Kevin walked away from the pitch.
He didn't want to stay where everyone was
angry with him.
He didn't know where he was going.
He just wanted to get away.

Kevin had been walking for quite a while.
He came to a canal.
A narrow-boat was tied to the bank.
It had its name painted on the side.
It was called the 'Mary Ann'.

'If I climb down the bank,' thought Kevin,
'I could jump onto the deck.'
He called 'Hello' to see if anyone was
on the boat, but no-one called back.
Kevin began to climb down the bank.
'This is more fun than playing football,'
he thought.

Mary Ann

The narrow-boat

When Kevin was half way down the bank, he gave
a big jump and landed on the deck of the boat.
Kevin looked around.
There were some steps going down into the cabin.

He went over to the steps and called out,
'Anyone there?'
No-one called back so Kevin went down the
steps into the cabin.

The cabin was small and very tidy.
On the table was a plate of sausage rolls.
Suddenly Kevin felt very hungry.
The sausage rolls looked good.
'Whoever lives on this boat won't miss a
sausage roll,' thought Kevin as he helped
himself to one.
It was very good, so he had three more!

While he was eating he looked around again.
At one end of the cabin was a bed.
Suddenly Kevin felt tired.
'I think I'll have a rest,' he thought.
'All that football has made me tired.'
Kevin had the last sausage roll,
lay down on the bed and fell asleep.

Very soon the owners of the narrow-boat came back.
'Time to go, Jack,' said Peg.
'Right, Peg,' said Jack.
Peg got onto the boat.
Jack untied the rope and pushed the boat
away from the bank.
Then he jumped on.
He switched on the engine.
The narrow-boat began to move along the canal.
Kevin was still asleep.

Jack began to sing and Peg sang with him.
The narrow-boat moved along the canal.
And Kevin was asleep in the cabin!

Where's Kevin?

Back at the football match things were
getting exciting.
Ripton Rovers got a goal.
Ben was fed up.
'Well,' said Rocky, 'we've only got ten players.'

The referee blew his whistle.
'Where's that boy I sent off?' he asked.
'He can come back now.'
The referee started the game again but there
was no sign of Kevin.
'Where IS that boy?' asked Mr March.
'I can't see him,' said Jamila.
'Go and look around the school,'
said Mr Belter to the girls.

Jamila and Tessa walked around the school but
they couldn't see Kevin anywhere.
'We'd better go back and tell Mr Belter
we can't find him,' said Tessa.

When the girls got back to the football pitch,
the match was over.
The teams had a goal each so it was a draw.
'Right,' said Mr March, 'get out of your
football gear, then you can have tea.'

Soon everyone was ready for tea.
'Well played, everyone,' said Mr Belter.
'Now have a good tea.'
Ben didn't feel like eating.
Ripton Rovers had got a goal.
He hadn't saved it.

'Kevin didn't come back to the match,
did he?' asked Rocky.
Mr Belter and Mr March were talking
about Kevin as well.
'I'll go and look for him while the kids
are having tea,' said Mr Belter.
'If we don't find him soon,' said Mr March,
'we'll have to report him missing to the police.'

Mr Belter went out to look for Kevin.
By this time the boat was a long way away.
Kevin had been asleep for a long time.
He suddenly woke up.
He could hear the noise of the engine.
'What's that noise?' he thought.
He looked out of the cabin window.
The boat was moving!
He could hear the engine and somebody singing.
'Oh, no!' he thought. 'The boat's moving!'

Kevin was afraid.
He knew there would be trouble if he was
found on the boat.
And he had eaten all the sausage rolls!
He had to get off the boat without being seen.
He looked out of the window again.
It was getting darker.
If only the boat would stop!

Suddenly the singing stopped.
Kevin heard people talking.
He crept to the door to listen.
'It's getting dark, Peg,' said Jack.
'Time to stop for the night. I'm hungry.'
'Oh, no!' thought Kevin.
'Are they coming in for their sausage rolls?'
Then Jack said, 'Let's walk into town.
I think I'll have a Chinese take-away.'
'OK,' said Peg, 'but I'll have fish and chips.'
Kevin waited until the people had
left the boat.
He came out of the cabin and up on deck.

Lost and found

Kevin looked around.
He didn't know where he was.
It was getting darker and he was lost!
He knew he had to get off the boat before
the people came back.

He climbed up the bank and began
to walk into town.
As he walked it got darker and darker.
Kevin felt cold.
He only had his football gear on.

'What am I going to do?' thought Kevin.
'I don't know where I am and I've no money to
telephone home!'
Kevin went on walking.
He looked at the street names but he didn't
know any of them.
He was feeling cold, tired and very frightened.

He came to a shop doorway and
sat down on the step.
'Mr Belter and Mr March will be looking
for me,' he thought.
But the teachers didn't know he had got on
the narrow-boat.
How would they ever find him?

CLOSED

Suddenly Kevin began to cry.
He wanted to go home.
He wished he had never left the football match.
That had been a stupid thing to do.

Then he heard footsteps.
Someone was coming.
The footsteps came nearer and nearer.
And then they stopped.
They stopped right in front of Kevin!

'Now then, lad. What are you doing out at
this time of night?'
Kevin looked up and saw a policeman.
'I'm lost,' he said. 'I want to go home.'
Kevin began crying again.
'OK, lad,' said the policeman. 'Don't cry.
We'll soon take you home.
You'd better come along to the police station and
you can tell me what happened!'

Kevin went with the policeman.
It was warm in the police station and
he was given a cup of tea.
'Now what's your name and where do you live?'
asked the policeman.
'I'm Kevin Miller and I live at number 25,
Wellington Square,' said Kevin.
'That's a good way from here,' said the policeman.
'What are you doing in this part of town?'

Kevin told him about the football match.
He told the policeman how he went to sleep
on the boat.
'When I woke up,' said Kevin, 'I didn't
know where I was.
I walked into the town but I couldn't
find Ripton School.
I've never been to this part of town before.'

'Right,' said the policeman.
'I'd better check to see if anyone has
reported you missing.
You just sit there and drink your tea.'
The policeman went away for a few minutes.

When he came back he said to Kevin,
'I called the police station near Ripton School.
Your teachers have been looking for you.
They reported you missing.
We've just telephoned your Mr Belter.
He's on his way over to get you.
You'll be OK now.'
Kevin looked worried.
He had been so pleased that the policeman
had found him, he had forgotten about Mr Belter!
He was going to be in trouble when he
came to get him!

After a while, Kevin saw Mr Belter's car pull
up outside the police station.
Ben and the twins were in the car too.
Mr Belter came into the police station.
He had been very worried about Kevin but
now he was looking pleased.

'I'm glad you're safe, Kevin,' he said.
'We were getting really worried about you.'
'Aren't I in trouble?' asked Kevin.
'Well,' said Mr Belter, 'I was very angry when
I couldn't find you but it's no good being cross now.
I think you've had enough trouble for one day!
A bit frightening being lost, eh?'

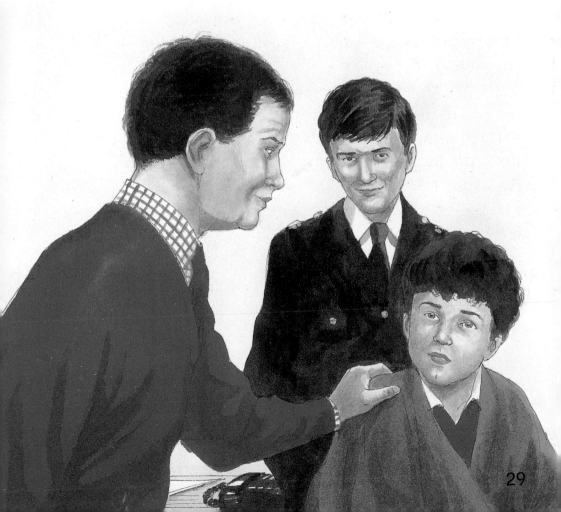

Kevin and Mr Belter left the police station.
As soon as he got in the car, Ben asked
Kevin what had happened.
He told them about the narrow-boat and
how he'd got lost.
'Bet you were scared,' said Ben.
'No, I wasn't,' said Kevin.
'Being out at night doesn't scare me!'

'Your Dad wasn't too pleased when he heard
you were lost,' said Tony.

'How does my Dad know?' asked Kevin.
'Mr Belter rang everyone's Mum and Dad.
He told them we were going to be a bit late,'
said Tessa.
'Then he took everyone home.
We wanted to come back to see what had
happened to you.'
Kevin was worried again.
What would his Dad say?

Kevin's Dad had a lot to say!
Kevin might not have been in trouble with
Mr Belter, but he WAS in trouble with his Dad!